# GOREY GAMES

D1230939

based on the works of

# EDWARD GOREY

games designed by

# LARRY EVANS

TROUBADOR PRESS  SAN FRANCISCO

# INTRODUCTION

For almost thirty years the meticulously drawn books of Edward Gorey have been read and collected by a loyal following of bemused fans. From the brooding mini-saga of all struggling authors, "The Unstrung Harp" (first published in 1953) to his more recent madness, "The Loathsome Couple," Edward Gorey has captured the macabre humor in the dark side of the human condition. His delightfully awesome, Tony Award-winning designs for the stage play "Dracula" had audiences applauding each time a new set was unveiled. "Dracula" also lifted Mr. Gorey's work from the felicity of fandom to rousing public acclaim.

Larry Evans has been bedeviling **his** fans with hundreds of puzzles, mazes and games published in a dozen books, as well as magazines, posters and art prints. His masterful use of perspective, exceptionally keen draftsmanship and warped turn of mind have earned Mr. Evans an internationally respected reputation as author, illustrator and puzzlesmith nonpareil.

A grand collaboration of Mr. Evans' talent and the fantastic creations that inhabit the fifty witty books of Mr. Gorey, this is the most unusual and exciting puzzlebook ever published. Troubador Press is proud to have played a part in bringing together these two geniuses (unstrung geniuses?). In any case we know that at least one of these characters was last seen going over the fence at the Weedhaven Laughing Academy.

Read on — you'll see why!

—Malcolm Whyte, Publisher

Library of Congress Cataloging in Publication Data

Gorey, Edward St. John.
    Gorey games.

    SUMMARY:  A collection of hidden picture puzzles,
codes, and mazes featuring macabre characters.
    1. Puzzles. 2. Games. [1. Puzzles] I. Evans,
Larry, 1939-        II. Title.
GV1493.G63        793.7'3        79-19054
ISBN 0-89844-000-9

# GOREY GAME 1

The author must take his walk through the maze to meet the author. Can you find a path that misses **all** the characters lurking in the shadows?

# GOREY GAME 2

A happy purveyor of underground containers. His business goes in the hole every day. What does this man do for a living?

# GOREY GAME 3

One Jumblie must ferry a pig, a monkey with lollypop paws and an owl, across the Western Sea in a sieve that can carry only one Jumblie and one animal. If the Jumblie leaves the pig alone with the owl, he will eat him. If he leaves the owl alone with the monkey, the owl will eat the monkey. How can the Jumblie ferry them all across the Western Sea?

# GOREY GAME 4

Which Fantod doesn't belong?

# GOREY GAME 5

In the west wing is a large box. In the box are six boxes, each contains three small boxes. How many boxes are in the west wing?

# GOREY GAME 6

Which girl's eye is closer to the eye of the young lady in the middle?

# GOREY GAME 7

*The* Cad

*The* Fetishist

*The* Xenophobe

Lord Stipple, Lord Irongate and Lord Legbail are known to all as a **cad**, a **xenophobe** and a **fetishist**, but not necessarily respectively. Given the following four clues, can you decide who is what? (By the way, three of the "clues" are lies.)

Lord Stipple is not a cad.

Lord Stipple is not the fetishist.

Lord Legbail is the fetishist.

Lord Legbail is not the cad.

# GOREY GAME 8

What will go down a chimney down, but not up a chimney up?

# GOREY GAME 9

The letters in this famous phrase from one of the Gorey stories have been altered to form a cypher. Each letter stands for another. See if you can decode this line.

**Qo oltstcjo, jdlrkre, id aruuqcr jqb hdar meda ojr qunsga.**
**— Ojr Dpfrho Sruudi.**

# GOREY GAME 10

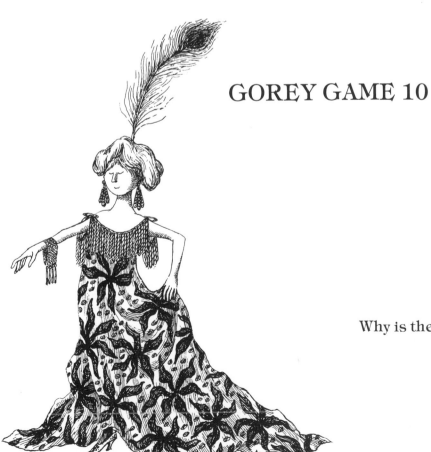

Why is the number 9 like a peacock?

Two beasties from the **Nursery Frieze** are twins. Can you find them?

# GOREY GAME 12

Find your way through the zagava tree
from the Osbick bird to Emblus Fingby.

# GOREY GAME 13

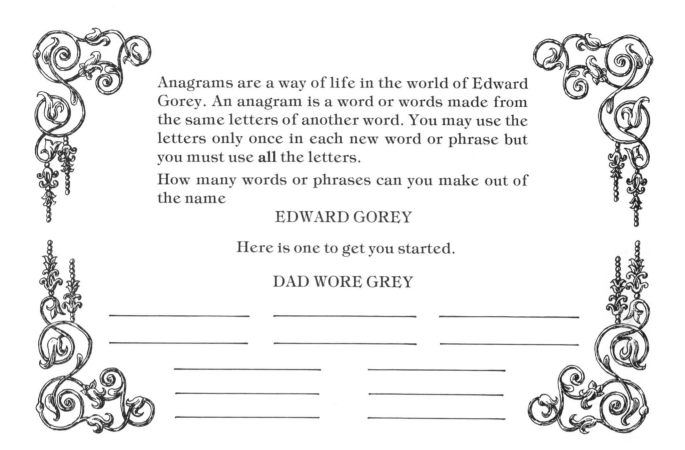

Anagrams are a way of life in the world of Edward Gorey. An anagram is a word or words made from the same letters of another word. You may use the letters only once in each new word or phrase but you must use **all** the letters.

How many words or phrases can you make out of the name

EDWARD GOREY

Here is one to get you started.

DAD WORE GREY

_____     _____     _____

_____     _____     _____

_____     _____

_____     _____

_____     _____

# GOREY GAME 14

What is the difference between a pitcher of water and Ida being thrown from a boat?

I is for IDA who drowned in a lake

# GOREY GAME 15

Hidden in these three drawings are: His Lordships' wooden leg, a bat (or an umbrella), a spyglass, a dinghy and a tea urn.

# GOREY GAME 16

A series of motor car races was held last Tuesday on the grounds of Backwater Hall. There were four races involving the same four motor cars. Each owner decided to drive a different car in each of the four races.

In the first race, Baron de Zabrus drove the Maharajah of Eschnapur's auto. In the second race, the Maharajah drove Dr. Belgravius' car. Basil Zaribaydjian won the third race in his own Bentover 12. Almost unbelievably, Basil won all of the races.

The swift Packard-Nash was driven by Dr. Belgravius in the second race, and by Baron de Zabrus in the final race. In the fourth race, the Packard-Nash was second to the Overbart-Thrush.

Who owns the Hover-Rover?

# GOREY GAME 17

Each numbered character below shares a panel in a Gorey book with a lettered character. Using the obvious (but subtle) clues, can you discover who matches whom?

A B C D E F

1 2 3 4 5 6

A goes with _____ B goes with _____ C goes with _____ D goes with _____

E goes with _____ F goes with _____

This scene from the **Deranged Cousins** is the famous Rabbit's Restroom. Do you think you can find eight differences in the two pictures?

# GOREY GAME 19

Which silhouette matches the drawing?

# GOREY GAME 20

How many people can you find in the box?

# GOREY GAME 21

How many cannonballs are in the pyramid?

On the opposite page are several letters followed by a verse. The trick here is to discover which verse goes with which panel.

**1** _____

**2** _____

**3** _____

X is for XERXES devoured by mice

4 ———

T is for TITUS who flew into bits

N is for NEVILLE who died of ennui

Y is for YORICK whose head was knocked in

C is for CLARA who wasted away

O is for OLIVE run through with an awl

V is for VICTOR squashed under a train

S is for SUSAN who perished of fits

Z is for ZILLAH who drank too much gin

L is for LEO who swallowed some tacks

H is for HECTOR done in by a thug

Q is for QUENTIN who sank in a mire

5 ———

# GOREY GAME 23

Connect the dots to discover a creature that shows no intention of going away.

# GOREY GAME 24

The little boy
with the sock
tells the truth.

I am not
a liar.

The man with
the sash is a liar.

The little boy
is a liar.

The little girl
is not a liar.

The preacher is
not a liar.

The maid
tells the truth.

The lady
with the box
never lies.

I am not
a liar.

The maid is
a liar.

Two of the characters above are liars. By deduction
discover who are liars.

# GOREY GAME 25

The squares on this page correspond to the chart on the next page. By transferring the lines to the proper areas in the chart you will be able to accurately draw a famous Gorey character.

Clue: His initials are B.B.

|   | A | B | C | D | E | F | G | H | J | K | L | M | N |
|----|---|---|---|---|---|---|---|---|---|---|---|---|---|
| 1  |   |   |   |   |   |   |   |   |   |   |   |   |   |
| 2  |   |   |   |   |   |   |   |   |   |   |   |   |   |
| 3  |   |   |   |   |   |   |   |   |   |   |   |   |   |
| 4  |   |   |   |   |   |   |   |   |   |   |   |   |   |
| 5  |   |   |   |   |   |   |   |   |   |   |   |   |   |
| 6  |   |   |   |   |   |   |   |   |   |   |   |   |   |
| 7  |   |   |   |   |   |   |   |   |   |   |   |   |   |
| 8  |   |   |   |   |   |   |   |   |   |   |   |   |   |
| 9  |   |   |   |   |   |   |   |   |   |   |   |   |   |
| 10 |   |   |   |   |   |   |   |   |   |   |   |   |   |
| 11 |   |   |   |   |   |   |   |   |   |   |   |   |   |
| 12 |   |   |   |   |   |   |   |   |   |   |   |   |   |
| 13 |   |   |   |   |   |   |   |   |   |   |   |   |   |

# GOREY GAME 26

Standing about at high tea with Grace Sprocket are six members of two notorious families of Violet Springs. One family, the Mousegraves, always tells the truth. The other family, The Sprigknots, always lies. Grace, upon endeavoring to ascertain the proper familial relationships between the assembled guests, asked each in turn just how many of them were Mousegraves. The first five answers were:

"Two of us are Mousegraves."

"One of us is a Mousegrave."

"Absolutely none of us is a Mousegrave."

"There are three Mousegraves here this afternoon."

"Three indeed, completely correct."

It was totally impossible for Grace to tell how many Mousegraves were at the party. However, the sixth guest, a dapper chap sporting a beard and a partial absence of hair on his head, quickly solved the problem for Grace by saying:

"There are none my dear, or perhaps there are six. Probably five. I can't be sure." How many Mousegraves were at high tea?

# GOREY GAME 27

Trace a path from Charlotte-Sophia to her loving father. Don't let the brute capture her or dreadful things will happen.

# GOREY GAME 28

How many complete
bats can you find in
the Japanese tapestry?

# GOREY GAME 29

How many sides
does a vase have?

# GOREY GAME 30

Dick Hammerclaw has chanced to meet three citizens of Chutney Falls.
Only two families live in Chutney Falls: the Underfoots (who always
lie) and the Blotters (who always tell the truth).
Dick would like to know whether he has run into Underfoots or Blotters,
so naturally he asks them who in fact they are.
"One of us is a Blotter," came the first reply.
"Absolutely true," came the second.
"Two of us are Blotters," was the third reply.
Just who were these people, Blotters or Underfoots?

# GOREY GAME 31

The eight panels on these two pages are from **The Listing Attic.**
Can you match the proper caption to the correct panels?

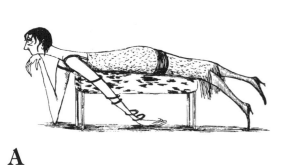

**A**

'My trip? It was vile. Balaclava
I loathed. Etna was crawling with lava.
    The ship was all white
    But it creaked in the night,
And the band, they did not know la java.'

**1**

**B**

Said a girl who upon her divan
Was attacked by a virile young man:
    'Such excess of passion
    Is quite out of fashion
And she fractured his wrist with her fan.

**2**

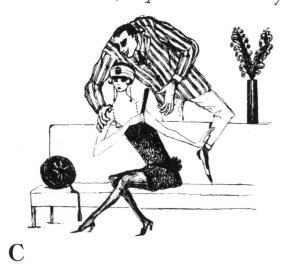

**C**

Pour guérir un accès de fièvre
Un jeune homme poursuivit un lièvre;
    Il le prit à son trou,
    Et fit faire un ragoût
Des entrailles et des pattes au genièvre.

**3**

**D**

Said Francesca, 'My lack of volition
Is leading me straight to perdition;
    But I haven't the strength
    To go to the length
Of making an act of contrition.'

**4**

**E**

At whist drives and strawberry teas
Fan would giggle and show off her knees;
   But when she was alone
**5**   She'd drink eau de cologne,
And weep from a sense of unease.

**F**

A gift was delivered to Laura
From a cousin who lived in Gomorrah;
   Wrapped in tissue and crepe,
**6**   It was peeled, like a grape,
And emitted a pale, greenish aura.

A goes with _____ B goes with _____ C goes with _____ D goes with _____ E goes with _____
F goes with _____ G goes with _____ H goes with _____

**G**

To a weepy young woman in Thrums
Her betrothed remarked, 'This is what comes
   Of allowing your tears
**7**   To fall into my ears—
I think they have rotted the drums.'

**H**

The partition of Vavasour Scowles
Was a sickener: they came on his bowels
   In a firkin; his brain
**8**   Was found clogging a drain,
And his toes were inside of some towels.

# GOREY GAME 32

The silhouette is a match to one of the authors below. See if you can tell which one. Mr. Gorey always wears his coat on his walks, so if you see a silhouette like this one be sure to say hello.

# GOREY GAME 33

Cut the circle into two equal parts, each containing six people.
Use straight lines only.

Climb through the maze from this page to the next, and find the salt herring.

# GOREY GAME 35

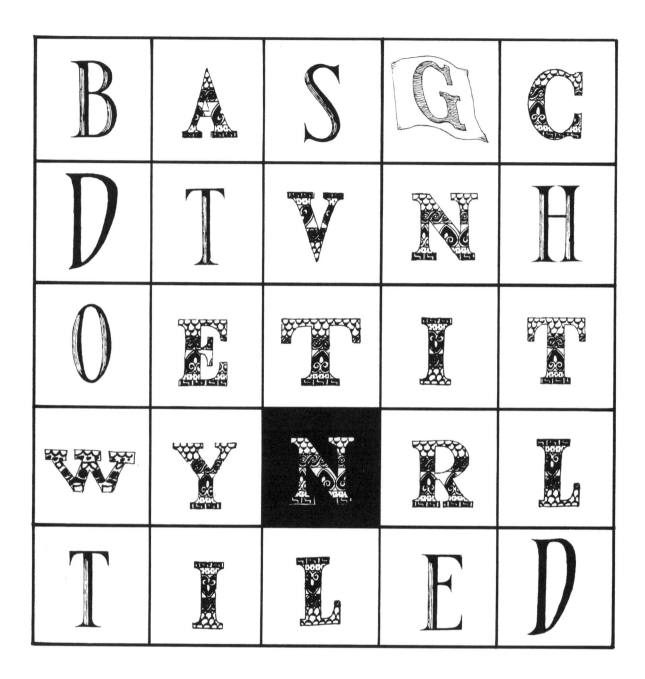

|   |   |   |   |   |
|---|---|---|---|---|
| B | A | S | G | C |
| D | T | V | N | H |
| O | E | T | I | T |
| W | Y | N | R | L |
| T | I | L | E | D |

Starting with the letter N (in the black box), and moving horizontally, diagonally or vertically, spell out the name of the book Beëlphazoar brought Miss Squill. You may re-use a letter but not more than one at a time. (In the olden days this was called a Knight's Move puzzle.)

The Dong with the Luminous Nose is trapped on the Square Island. The Jumblie wants to help him but the two boards are a little bit too short to reach across the moat. Without using nails or glue or anything like that, can you figure out how the Jumblie can rescue the Dong?

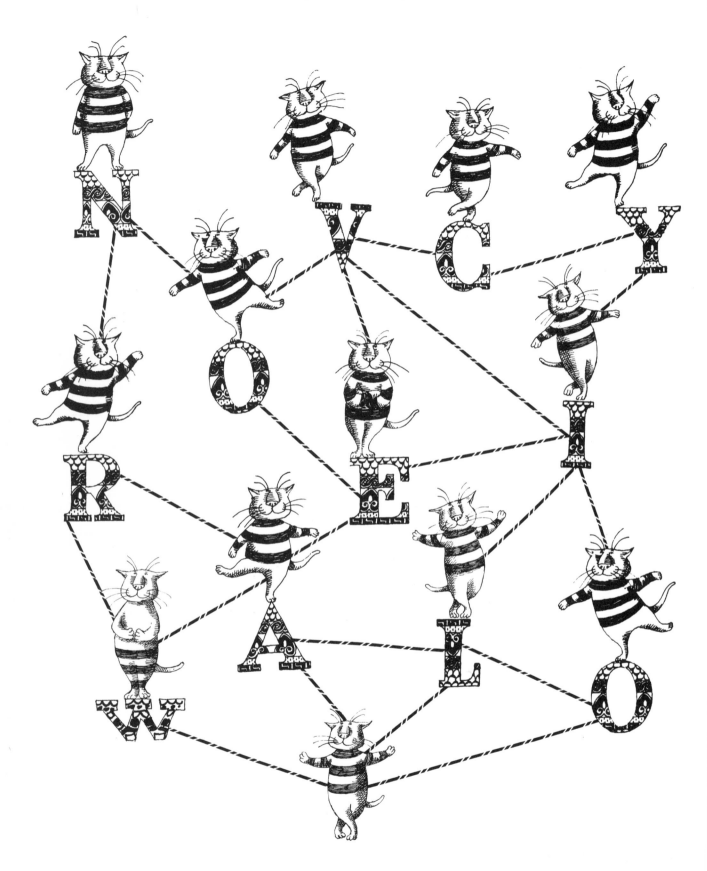

Starting with the bottom cat, trace a path from letter to letter to spell out the name of one of the Gorey kids from the **Gashlycrumb Tinies**. This person's name just might appear in Game 22.

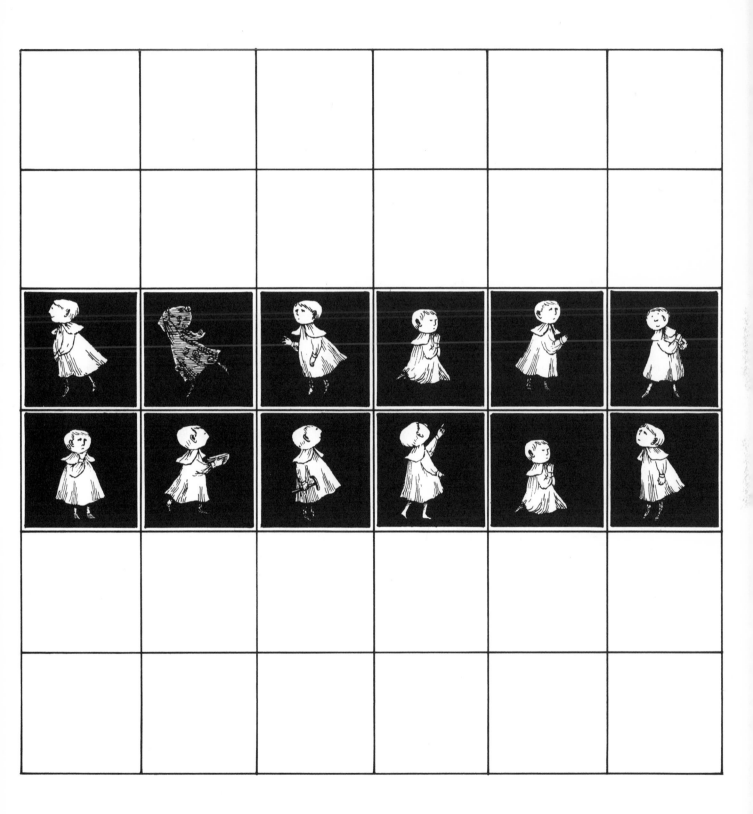

Rearrange the twelve Pious Infants so that there
will be two on each row, horizontal, vertical and
diagonal, **but** no more than two in any straight line.

# GOREY GAME 39

The four cats on page 39 are from the four panels illustrated on these two pages. See if you can discover which cat belongs in which panel. The backgrounds have been blacked out and the squares changed in size to make this puzzle **easier** for you.

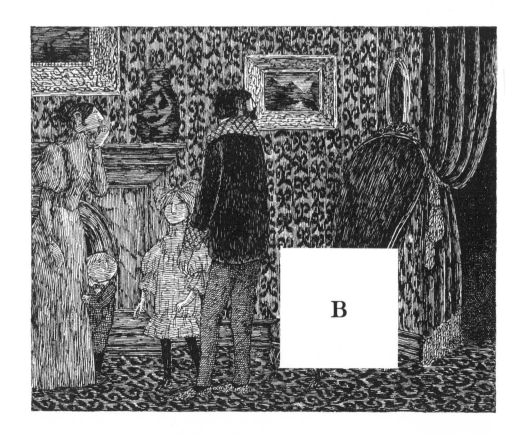

C

D

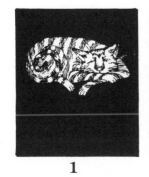

1

2

3

4

# GOREY GAME 40

Dracula has assumed a negative posture in the upper
left corner. Discover if you can, which Dracula is the
positive (direct opposite) of the negative.

# GOREY GAME 41

Mr. Earbrass coughed nervously and set down the book he was reading (A Compendium of the Minor Heresies of the Twelfth Century in Asia Minor) as the two figures entered the room.

"My goodness, aren't you the treasurer of Scuffle and Dustcough, my publishers?"

"Why, yes I am," came the reply.

"I haven't seen you in years, and this little girl with you," he asked, "is she yours?"

"She certainly is. You didn't know I was married, did you?"

"What is your name, child?" asked Mr. Earbrass.

"Drusilla," came the reply.

"Why," exclaimed Mr. Earbrass, "that's the same name as your mother."

Now how did he know that?

# GOREY GAME 42

If four cats and three kittens weigh 37 pounds, and three cats and four kittens weigh 33 pounds, how much does a cat weigh? How much does a kitten weigh?

There are at least eight differences between these two pictures from **The Guilded Bat**. Can you find them all?

# GOREY GAME 44

| S | L | C | R | O | R | R | O | h | T | A | O | L |
|---|---|---|---|---|---|---|---|---|---|---|---|---|
| H | D | I | M | V | e | u | S | L | E | E | C | H |
| R | e | T | O | S | M | I | o | f | C | h | D | u |
| I | N | O | O | L | u | F | T | E | R | f | E | T |
| E | W | R | D | G | L | N | n | u | e | b | t | p |
| K | O | E | n | L | Y | E | A | N | E | C | L | m |
| m | R | A | U | H | S | C | N | A | p | H | u | u |
| D | D | y | R | l | A | u | d | e | i | D | A | L |
| E | b | F | i | L | I | E | A | G | N | D | s | A |
| K | H | M | y | l | t | 5 | A | H | G | O | 5 | G |
| O | E | O | E | D | I | C | I | U | S | o | A | u |
| H | E | L | A | P | M | I | H | f | U | L | N | L |
| c | D | E | R | E | h | T | O | M | S | B | E | G |

Hidden in the graph are the following words. To find them all, you may read horizontally, diagonally, vertically, frontwards and backwards. One word has already been circled to get you started.

ASYLUM    ANGUISH    BLOOD    CHOKED    CREEPING    DIED    DOOM
DROWNED    ENNUI    EROTIC    FRETFUL    ASSAULTED    MOROSE
GLUGALUMP    SLIME    HORROR    GHASTLY    SMOTHERED    THUG
LEECH    IMPALE    SUICIDE    SHRIEK    LOATH

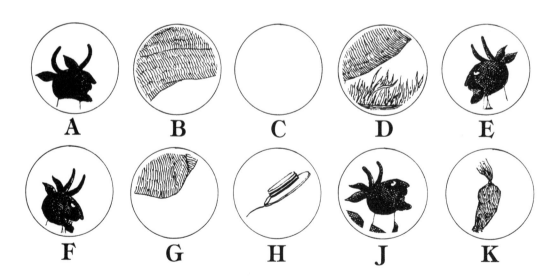

Three circles have been removed from the drawing. See if you can put the correct circle in its proper place.

# GOREY GAME 46

As the party was about to retire for the night Fenks announced
that the _____ _____ was not in its case.

Starting with the proper letter and counting every fourth letter, (i.e., B-O) **and** counting
the small circle, spell out the name of the missing object in the picture caption.

# GOREY GAME 47

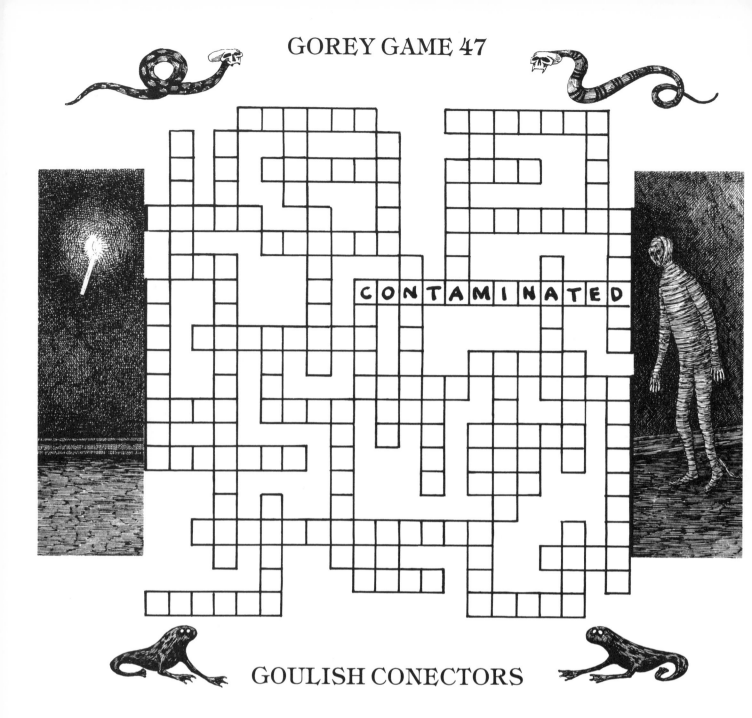

CONTAMINATED

## GOULISH CONECTORS

Insert the words below into this diagram either vertically or horizontally. One word has been placed for you. The words have been arranged into groups of three letter, four letter, etc., to aid you in your task.

THREE LETTER  Axe Mad Lye Mar Pry God Zoo Odd  Try Ump Old
FOUR LETTER Mean Dead Gasp Kill Thug Odor Fits Wing Sock Rots Thip
FIVE LETTERS Beast Elbow Moldy Utter Swamp Bleak Swoon Chasm Demon Weird Agony
SIX LETTERS Beware Unwell Yorick Wuggly Scream Miasma Sludge Fantod
SEVEN LETTERS Hapless Dracula Cripple Ungodly Leotard Listing
EIGHT LETTERS Abandons Drusilla Deranged
NINE LETTERS Dustcough
TWELVE LETTERS Contaminated
THIRTEEN LETTERS Disrespectful Quoggenzocker

# GOREY GAME 48

Using ten glass telephone pole insulators from the vast collection of Zeph Claggs, arrange them so that there will be five rows with four insulators in each row.

# GOREY GAME 49

If a young lady fell into a well, why wouldn't her brother help her out?

# GOREY GAME 50

Mr Gorey, Mr Earbrass, and a Knowledgeable Friend.

Mr. Gorey, Mr. Earbrass and a Knowledgeable Friend are all wearing caps. These extra-ordinary hats were chosen out of five by yet another friend, Mrs. Regera Dowdy. Three of the hats were red and two yellow. After looking at each other for a few minutes, Mr. Earbrass said, "I surely can't decide what color my hat is."
The Knowledgeable Friend frowned and finally said, "For the life of me I can't decide what color my cap is."
Mr. Gorey then smiled his famous smile and said, "My cap is red."
Now, how could he possibly have known that?

# GOREY GAME 51

Here is cypher No. 2. See Gorey Game 9 for instructions.

**Zeudpqtp hxt deuq sbco guec sbco ow dzp edzpu iribst.**
**—Dzp Zxisptt Azbste.**

48

# GOREY GAME 52

Color in the areas with dots and then
see if you can find the Wuggly Ump.

In these scenes from **The Gilded Bat** two ballet dancers are hidden from view. Also concealed is the bat costume Maudie wore. See if you can find these things and, while you're at it, find **a champagne glass** with an olive in it.

# GOREY GAME 54

Add up the proper ballet dancers to a total of 50.

Seated around the breakfast table are a ubiquitous group of relatives and an obvious outsider with the last name of Guest. Your job is to discover who is who, and who is sitting next to whom.

Mr. Grewdead sits two places to the left of Ortenzia.

Dedge sits two places to the right of Miss Caviglia. Mr. Dogyear is on Roy's left and Agnes-Alice is on Roy's right.

Drew is to the right of Mr. Dogyear's half nephew, Mr. Yarrow.

Mr. Guest is on Dedge's left.

Miss Popover sits directly opposite Dedge.

Doubtful sits two seats away from Agnes-Alice.

# GOREY GAME 56

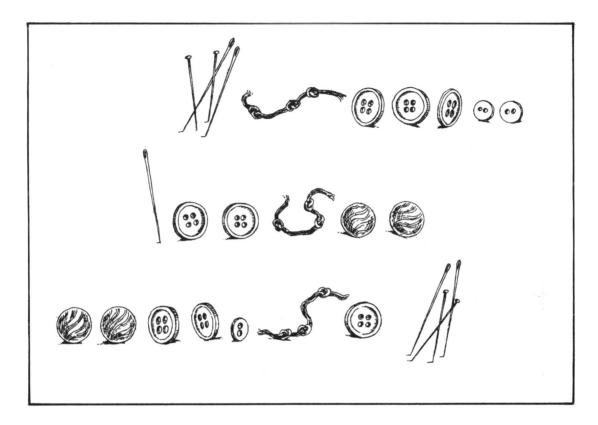

Four pins from **The Inanimate Tragedy** are equal in tug o'war to five buttons. The knotted string indicates the tug o'war rope. One pin and two buttons are equal to two marbles. Who would win a tug o'war with two marbles and three buttons against one button and four pins?

# GOREY GAME 57

How many bugs would it take to balance the teeter-totter if all the Jumblies were on one side?

# GOREY GAME 58

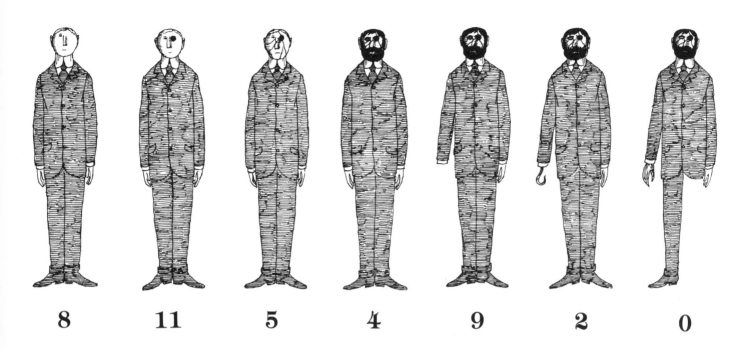

Private eye Waredo Dyrge, a former soldier of fortune and progressive victim of explosions all over the world, wishes to know just what is the relationship of the series of numbers above?

# GOREY GAME 59

Cypher No. 3. See Gorey Game 9 for instructions.

**Meiku ipkn pmo qmi ofgd, ouhqayym qmg ipmi cu. xumbhk gfuk df qfxvq.**

**— Ipk Ukckczkuko Jaqai**

# GOREY GAME 60

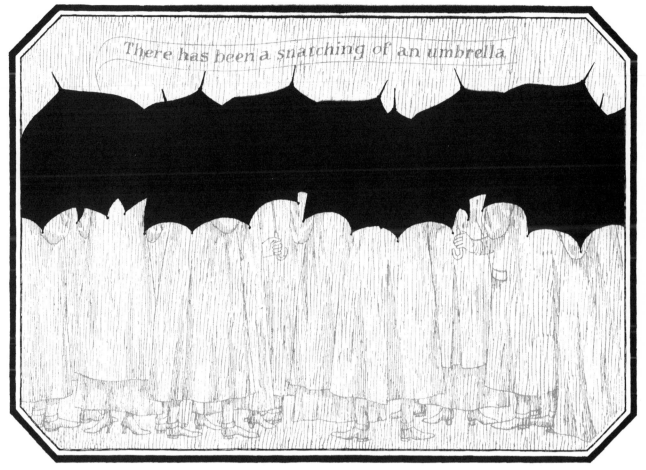

How many umbrellas, either whole or in part, can you count in this panel? How many people?

# GOREY GAME 61

Without using a pencil can you quickly tell which maze Waredo Dyrge should take to escape from yet another explosion?

# GOREY GAME 62

The guests from **The Curious Sofa** have arranged themselves on the floor in a very creative way. However, one of the guests seems to be missing. Can you discover who has left the party? Some are used more than once. It's that kind of party.

# GOREY GAME 63

## LOVE STORY

Four cousins and four other foul persons (four men and four women) are standing about after brunch. Each male hates a female and is hated in turn by either one cousin (either male or female) or one foul person.

Marsh Maryrose hates a lady who absolutely despises Lord Stipple. Lord Irongate abhors a girl who is totally disgusted with the man who intends to kill Miss Fleager. Mary Rosemarsh has her blood curdled by the man who is about to be murdered by the girl who is hated by Dick Hammerclaw. Maudie loves Dick Hammerclaw and is loved in turn by the man who Nellie is going to disembowel.

Who hates Lord Irongate enough to kill him?

> This is a tough puzzle. Here are some added clues:
> Marsh is a man.
> Mary Rosemarsh is hated by the man who is her cousin in
> the book "The Derranged Cousins."

# GOREY GAME 64

It is 10 miles between Hiccupboro and the Weedhaven Laughing Academy. How many young ladies would it take to reach from Hiccupboro to the Academy?

# GOREY GAME 65

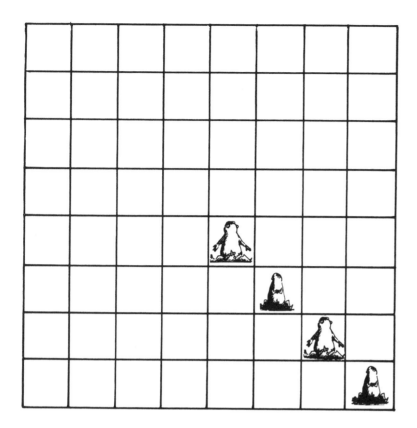

Divide the chart into four pieces so that each of the four parts will be exactly the same shape and, so that each part will contain a Beastly Baby.

# GOREY GAME 66

Find a path from the bottom to the top using only **two** straight lines. Don't touch a monster or else!

# GOREY GAME 67

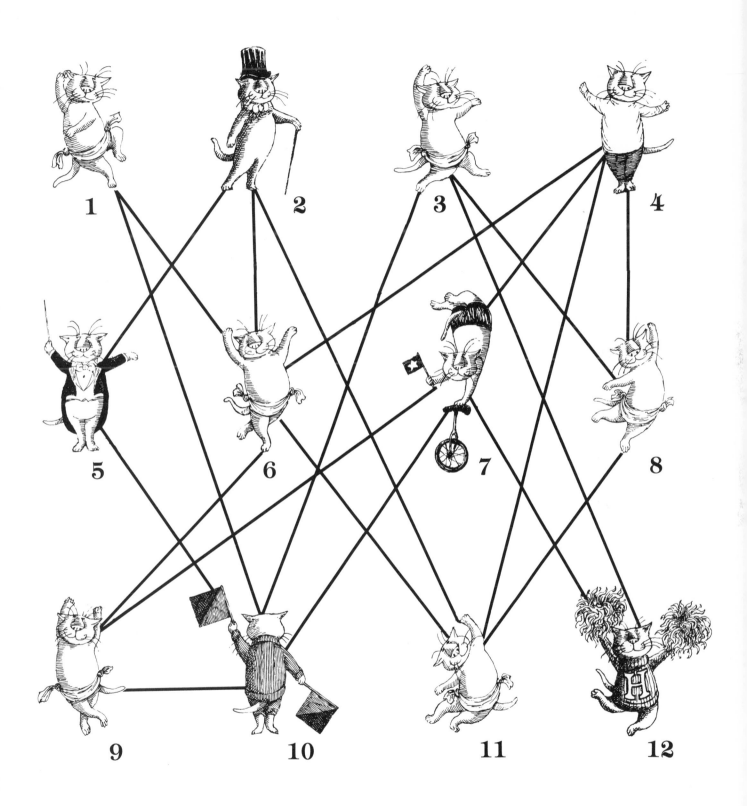

Discover the fastest route from cat number one to
cat 12 touching each cat only once.

# GOREY GAME 68

## GOREY CROSSWORD PUZZLE DEFINITIONS

### ACROSS

1. "Story for _____"
5. This had to be done many times to "Prue trampled flat in a brawl." —see 73 across.
10. Another word for 54 down
14. Cooler
15. City in Florida
16. Genus of auk
17. The light reflected from the Bong-tree by the luminous nose of the Dong did this
20. **Beginning of quote: 3 wds.**
25. Mrs. Regera Dowdy probably used this poetic form of "over" in her poetry
26. Small fish
27. Dracula by night
28. The Beastly Baby's mother _____ the day he was born: regrets
29. Orkney inlet
30. Another word for the cad who decides "he has grown weary of affair and that is that.": **The Fatal Lozenge**
32. Scottish word for the snow that obscured the way the others wish to go
34. The bicycle bandit does this to the Marchioness of Bunworry's emeralds during a ball at Condiment House: slang
35. "D" is for Desmond thrown _____ of a sleigh" —see 73 across.
36. Larry _____, author of several books on mazes and games
38. Proceed briskly
41. The ballerina Mirella Splatova wore her hair pulled back into a knot in the shape of a _____ .
42. Hamish kept a voluminous diary in which to _____: "**The Lost Lions**"
44. Another word to describe the "shouting" that tells the quarry "they are out for blood." — "**The Fatal Lozenge**"
45. **Second part of quote: 2 wds.**
47. "G is for George smothered _____ a rug" —see 73 across.
48. When a "young woman named Rose, who fainted whenever she chose, was revived by a hose," she must have been all _____: **The Listing Attic**
51. The bugs in "**The Bug Book**" come in three of these
52. **Third part of quote: 1 wd.**
54. One of the Deranged Cousins
58. "I hear them walking about on the ceiling. _____ had gone irretrievably out of her head.": "**The Insect God**"

60. Map abbr. — abbr. of 23 down
61. "At Wunksieville they rescued an infant who was _____ing from a hook intended for mailbags.": **The Willowdale Handcar**
62. "Thip, thap, _____o.": **The Untitled Book**
65. Celebes ox
66. Mr. Queevil _____ soda pop and gingersnaps at his Bogus Corners Store
68. The _____ Lozenge
69. The two yellow bugs had three cousins this color
70. In **The Curious Sofa** Alice continually _____ her virtue
72. Scuffle and Dustcough must _____ Mr. Earbrass' manuscript of **The Unstrung Harp** before it can be published
73. "The _____lycrumb Tinies"
74. Surrender
76. Female saint: abbr.
77. Charlotte-Sophia's parents were well-to-do and could be considered part of this group
79. Grotesquely ludicrous action
81. **The Willow_____ Handcar**
82. **Fourth part of quote: 1 wd.**
83. Moslem counterpart of the Maharajah
84. This is what the big black bug in **The Bug Book** might have been: type of beetle
86. Yoko _____, ex-wife of an ex-Beatle
87. "The gorgeous flowers have a smell that causes one to feel unwell": another word for smell, see 50 & 73 down
88. "She became aware of what _____ ballet was when Madame took her to one of Solepsiskaya's innumerable farewell performances." — **The Gilded Bat**
89. Miss Splaytoe's namesakes
91. **Fifth part of quote: 1 wd.**
93. The hapless tot is _____ when the Zouave impales it with a sword
96. This amount of rain caused the infant in **The Sopping Thursday** to be swept into an open sewer
98. "In spite of their praiseworthy efforts, then _____ with nothing at all in the way of news.": **The Insect God**
103. What fraternity members wear to toga parties
104. Island: French
105. Comedian Louis _____ and family
107. Major artery
108. The people in the dinghy in **The Object Lesson** could use one of these

109. Word for the abnormal development of Miss Squill's plants that gave out screams and sighs
111. "On _____ 18th of alternate years Mr. Earbrass begins writing 'his new novel'.": abbr. —**The Unstrung Harp**
113. Mr. Earbrass hums themes from "Poddington Te _____"
114. Shoshonean Indian
115. The cat who swallowed the heroine in — 1 across, "went off contently licking his chops," and probably emitting this sound
116. School of higher learning in the South: abbr.
119. The Glass Marble in **The Inanimate Tragedy** could be one of these
121. Girl's name
122. **Sixth part of quote: 4 wds.**
126. Word for the devil who left the mark on Miss Squill's breast
128. Radar screen image
129. "The abduction of _____ Thrudd on August the 6th, 1907.": **The Broken Spoke**
130. "_____ was crawling with lava": **The Listing Attic**
131. Fruit decay
132. So. Africans of Dutch descent
133. **Final word of quote**

### DOWN

1. The Pious Infant prayed day and night that he wouldn't commit one of these
2. Beginning of the Broadway play "Dracula"
3. "The Quarry, fleeing from the outing, sinks painting in the _____ and mud": see 68 across —The _____ Lozenge
4. Henry Clump's devotion could be described this way
5. ". . . a dark bearded man from a ghetto slipped forward and grabbed her tresses and _____bed her to death with a rusty stiletto,": **The Listing Attic**
6. So. African weaver bird
7. Mr. Earbrass had to _____ parts of his book when he revised it: leave out
8. Army lawmen: abbr.
9. "The Baron chose her to dance a new _____ de deux.": **The Guilded Bat**
10. If left outside after _____ the Beastly Baby will turn a horrid purple: dawn
11. Harry _____ his friends to go for a ride on a handcar: insists
12. _____ Awdrey-Gore
13. At the end of each arm the monkey has a lollypop _____: **The Jumblies**

17. The real, Tony Award-winning, author of **The Unstrung Harp**
18. The Doubtful Guest never showed any inclination to _____ : go away
19. . . . If Mr. Alda is in a bad mood, his friends might say "Don't _____ _____ : 2 wds.
21. Satire
22. After a game of double solitaire, Emblus Fingby and the Osbick Bird would _____ each other for a week
23. The map in **The Awdrey-Gore Legacy** traces the _____ of the suspects
24. The poetess Mrs. Regera Dowdy would be concerned with this
31. Photographic term: abbr.
33. Nigerian native
34. Surly and cowardly fellows, drunken brutes
37. Compass reading
39. Another word that could be used by Mrs. Regera Dowdy in her poetry: many times
40. When Marsh Maryrose drank the dregs of a bottle of vanilla extract it did more than slake his _____ .
41. Given half a chance, Dracula would do this, to your neck.
42. The _____ Ump
43. Nurses: abbr.
46. Food for an aardvark
49. "_____ is for Susan who perished of fits.": see **73 across**
50. **First 2 words of title containing the quote**
52. Mr. Earbrass uses a loofah when doing this
53. "U is for _____ who slipped down a drain.": see **73 across**
54. "They lived in a house covered with roses on the edge of a _____ ." —**The Derranged Cousins**
55. Miss Loos, author of "Gentlemen Prefer Blondes"
56. Namesakes of one of the Deranged Cousins
57. Talk, chatter
59. Descriptive of Mr. Crague in **The Remembered Visit**
61. Mr. Earbrass _____ _____ revise TUH before taking it to Scuffle and Dustcough: 2 wds.
62. Part of the stairs on which Glassglue appeared to Mr. Earbrass: stair part
63. Greeting
64. More peculiar and strange
67. French lily
68. "At whist drives and strawberry teas _____ would giggle and show off her knees.": **The Listing Attic**

Crossword Puzzle designed by Rosalee Evans

71. Highlights
73. **Last word of title quoted**
74. Two words said on the wedding day
78. Dr. Assoc: abbr.
80. Bill and _____
84. Challenge
85. Possessive pronoun
88. Small creek
89. Mildew, fungus
90. Ship's curved plank
92. "The top of the zagava tree was frequently where they had _____ .": **The Osbick Bird**
93. Because of their size, the Beastly Baby and a certain young man in **The Listing Attic** could be described by this word
94. "Balaclava I _____ ed,": from the same verse as **130 across**: **The Listing Attic**
95. Concur
96. The Marchioness of Bunworry might wear one of these on her head
97. Two more than the total number of bugs in **The Bug Book**
99. Sign of assent
100. "Each night father fills me with _____ when he sits on the foot of my bed.": **The Listing Attic**

101. Musical piece
102. Hard resin
106. A word to describe **The West Wing**
109. _____ Blake, American composer, pianist
110. Where Dracula would like to have his body kept in the daytime.
112. This word might describe the "unnerving silver-gilt combination epergne and candelabrum" Mr. Earbrass received from an admirer: **The Unstrung Harp**
115. This might cover Dracula's coffin
116. "Lady Celia's French maid, _____ .": **The Curious Sofa**
117. Bother or fuss
118. "He _____ a hammer heavy, heavy, heavy to drive the nail into the wall: **The Salt Herring**
120. The sound of the Beastly Baby's demise
123. Business mens assoc.: abbr.
124. The Osbick Bird has a big one
125. "An Apparition of her lover she recognizes with dismay; and later on she will discover that he himself had died today.": Her lovers mail will end up in this dept. of the Post Office, abbr.: **The Fatal Lozenge**
127. Has not; old English

61

# SOLUTIONS

**1.**

**2.** Undertaker

**3.** The Jumblie must start with the owl, as the pig won't bother the monkey. He leaves the owl on the other side and returns. He then puts the monkey in the boat and takes him across, leaves him and brings the owl back. He leaves the owl and takes the pig. He leaves the pig with the monkey and rows back, picks up the owl and ferrys him across.

**4.** The second from the left. Fantods don't wear tennis shoes. Besides, all the others are twins or triplets.

**5.** 25

**6.** The eyes are the same distance.

**7.** Either clue 1 or 2 must be true. If 2 is true, 4 and 1 must be true. Therefore, 1 is the true statement. Lord Legbail is the cad. Lord Stipple is the fetishist and Lord Irongate is the xenophobe.

**8.** An umbrella

**9.** CYPHER 1
At twilight, however, no message had come from the asylum.
The Object Lesson

**10.** Because without its tail it's nothing.

**11.** Beastie no. 2 in the third line from the top on p. 8 and beastie no. 2, third line from the top on p. 9.

**12.**

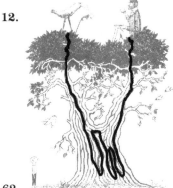

**13.** Here are a few of the better anagrams we found:
WE GRADED ROY
YE GOD REWARD
GOYA DREW RED
EDY WORE DRAG
GROW DEAD RYE
DRAY OR WEDGE?
A GREEDY WORD
WEARY RED GOD
ORDER A WEDGY
O' EDGY DRAWER

**14.** One is "to pitch her in the water." The other is a pitcher of water.

**15.**

**16.** To solve this puzzle, let B stand for Basil, D for Dr. Belgravius, M for the Maharajah and Z, for Baron de Zabrus. Their autos then can be b, d, m, and z. Let x stand for the Packard-Nash. Obviously x is neither d nor m and cannot be b, so the Packard-Nash is owned by Baron de Zabrus. Basil owns the Bentover 12 and the Overbart-Thrush is owned by Dr. Belgravius (driven by Basil in the fourth race). The Hover-Rover must be owned by the Maharajah.

**17.** A-2, B-5, C-6, D-1, E-4, F-3

**18.** IN THE BOTTOM PICTURE
No H on sweater
Steeple has moved to left
Lady's socks are white
Lady has long hair
Lady's hat has black band
Weed is missing
Man's hand is behind him
Circles are gone from lady's and man's shoes.

**19.** Third from the left, second row.

**20.** 10 people, notice little boy in man's lap and man behind curtain

**21.** 117

**22.** 1-Z, 2-N, 3-S, 4-Y, 5-T.

**23.**

**24.** The maid and the man with the sash are liars.

**25.** THE BEASTLY BABY

**26.** The answer, "none of us is a Mousegrave," must be given by a Sprigknot, so it is obviously a lie. At least one guest is a Mousegrave. With one answer yet to come, you might find one, two or even three Mousegraves at high tea. The only answer possible to give us an absolute figure has to be: Six, five, four or none, because an answer of three, two or one gives an inconclusive number. There was ONE Mousegrave at high tea.

**27.**

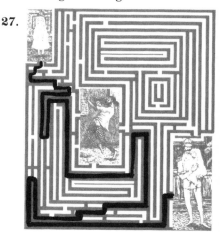

**28.** 9 bats

**29.** Two-the inside and the outside.

# SOLUTIONS

**30.** From statement one, we must assume that three is a liar. From statement two, we re-enforce our belief that three is a liar. However, if there are two Blotters, then one and two are liars. And, if there is only one, then one and two are telling the truth. THAT is impossible.
ALL the citizens must be Underfoots.

**31.** A-4, B-5, C-2, D-7, E-3, F-8, G-6, H-1.

**32.** The first drawing, bottom row.

**33.**

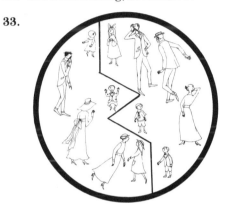

**34.**

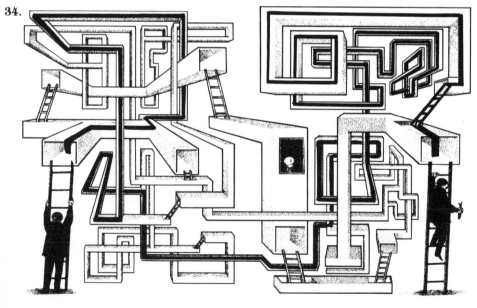

**35.** Ninety Two Entirely Evil Things To Do.

**36.** THE ISLAND SOLUTION

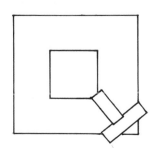

**37.** OLIVE

**38.** HERE IS ONE SOLUTION

**39.** A-4, B-3, C-1, D-2.

**40.** The second Dracula in the second row right.

**41.** The treasurer of Scuffle and Dustcough was a WOMAN.

**42.** CAT = 7lbs., KITTEN = 3lbs.

**43.** IN THE SECOND PICTURE
Man is missing
Peak on left is different
Extra feather in headdress
Star is missing
Black ballet shoes
Strap is missing
Shine is gone from hair
Bangles on tutu are missing
Necklace added
Smile

**44.**

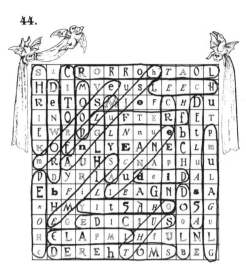

**45.** 1-F, 2-D, 3-C.

**46.** LISPING ELBOW

**47.**

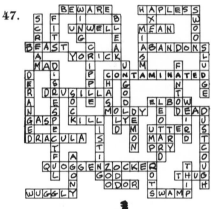

**48.**

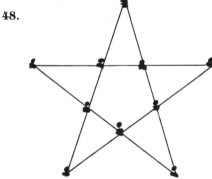

**49.** Because he couldn't be her brother and assist her (a sister) too.

**50.** Mr. Earbrass could not have seen 2 yellow caps so he had no idea. The friend reasoned that Mr. Earbrass could not tell his own color so it was not obvious what his color was either. Mr. Gorey knew that both companions would have been able to guess their own color if **his** cap had been yellow. He knew, then that his own cap must be red.

**51.** CYPHER 2
Hortense was torn limb from limb by the other pupils.
The Hapless Child

# SOLUTIONS

**52. THE WUGGLY UMP**

**53.**

**54.** 25 + 6 + 19 = 50

**55.** Draw a diagram of the table. Starting with ANY statement, you will find the seating arrangement is (in clockwise order), Roy Grewdead, Drew Dogyear, Dedge Yarrow, Doubtful Guest, Ortenzia Caviglia and Agnes-Alice Popover.

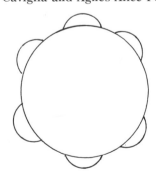

**56.** The two marbles and three buttons would win.

**57.** 12 bugs

**58.** The numbers are in alphabetical order.

**59.** CYPHER 3
After they had sat down, Drusilla saw that Mr. Crague wore no socks.
The Remembered Visit

**60.** 12 people
12 umbrellas

**61.** The left maze is the exit.

**62.** The peg-leg lady is missing.

**65.**

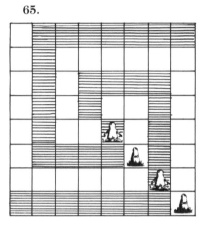

**63.** Maudie-the dialog reads in sequence-Marsh hates Mary who hates Lord Stipple. Lord Irongate hates Nellie who hates Dick, who hates Miss Fleager. Mary is hated by Marsh who is hated by Miss Fleager who is hated by Dick Hammerclaw. Maudie loves Dick and is loved by Dick who is hated by Nellie. Lord Irongate is hated by Maudie.

**64.** 10; Because a miss is as good as a mile!

**66.**

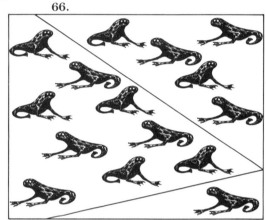

**67.** 1-6, 6-2, 2-5, 5-10, 10-9, 9-7, 7-4, 4-11, 11-8, 8-3, 3-12.

**68. CROSSWORD PUZZLE SOLUTION**

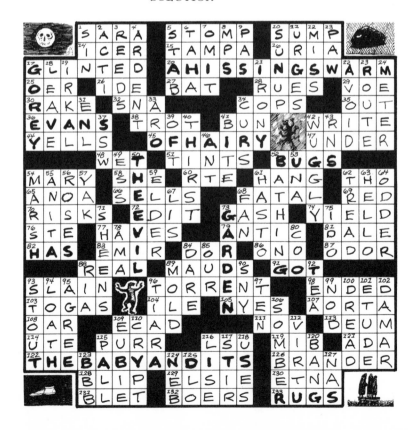